Fun with the Funnies

Fun with the Funnies

50 MOTIVATING ACTIVITIES FOR LANGUAGE ARTS, WRITING, AND SOCIAL STUDIES, GRADES 4-6

JOHN GUENTHER

Professor of Curriculum and Instruction
The University of Kansas

ILLUSTRATED BY **SYLVIA STONE**

Scott, Foresman and Company
Glenview, Illinois
Dallas, Texas   Oakland, New Jersey
Palo Alto, California   Tucker, Georgia
London

ACKNOWLEDGMENTS

I wish to acknowledge the continuing friendship and support of other newspaper-in-education professionals. I am indebted in particular to the NIE staff of the American Newspaper Publishers Association. A special thanks is due Mr. John Stauffer, editor and publisher of the *Topeka Capital-Journal,* for his enlightened commitment to NIE programs.

To my cast of characters:
Norma, Lynn, Jane, and Susan

ISBN: 0-673-15637-0

123456-MAL-888786858483

Contents

PART I

Language Arts/Creative Writing   1

PART II

Current Events/Human Behavior   31

Program Overview

More and more educators are discovering the positive benefits of using the daily newspaper in the classroom. Educationally sound newspaper activities are supplementing the use of more traditional text materials in most subject areas and at most grade levels. As a classroom resource, the newspaper is relevant, comprehensible, colorful, fresh, up-to-date, inexpensive, and motivating. Although all sections of a newspaper can be used as learning aids, the section that may have the most appeal is the comic-strip section. Comic strips have been found to be extremely effective in teaching a wide variety of concepts and skills. Although comic-strip activities can be designed for all students, they have been used most successfully with students who lack motivation and/or are below average in ability.

More specifically, newspaper comic strips serve as a valuable instructional aid for the following reasons:

1. They are a real part of the student's culture and, as such, are intrinsically motivating; they are read by a majority of students and adults.
2. They reflect our culture and mirror the issues and events of our daily lives.
3. They are interesting, easy to read, compact in thought, simple, and colorful, and they include subject matter that deals with a full range of human emotions.
4. They are informative, consumable, and universally available.
5. They help bridge the gap between the visual medium of television and conventional print material.
6. They appeal to all ages and levels of American society.

As with the use of all teaching aids, our goals and objectives must determine the validity of using comic strips in the classroom. It makes sense, in any event, to consider the use of any resource that is considered relevant to students and might motivate them to learn. It has been said that the key to learning is motivation, and the key to motivation is relevancy.

This book contains fifty comic-strip activity sheets. Each activity has a clearly defined objective stated in question form. When possible, the activities are sequenced by level of difficulty. Some activities are interrelated, whereas others are independent. The program has been designed so that the activities can be completed or done only in part, depending on the instructional needs of the teacher.

The activities are organized into the following basic subject, or topic, areas:

Part I: Language Arts/Creative Writing
Part II: Current Events/Human Behavior

The activities, although designed for use primarily with grades four through six, are suitable for students in the total span of middle-level education. All activities are written directly to the student and can be used with a variety of instructional approaches.

Good Luck and Have Fun.

Program Activities and Objectives

PART I: Language Arts/Creative Writing

ACTIVITY	OBJECTIVE
Parts of Speech	Identify various parts of speech
Adjectives Describe	Select adjectives to describe characters
Words, Words, Words	Define unfamiliar words
Poor Grammar	Find examples of poor grammar
Substituting Synonyms	Select synonyms for various words
Main Ideas	Identify main ideas from comic-strip stories
Headlines	Summarize stories by writing headlines
Character Traits	Identify character traits
Character Charts	Identify various kinds of character types
Character Sketches	Develop character sketches
Obituary	Analyze one or more comic-strip characters
Novels or Short Stories	Describe the elements of novels or short stories
Summary Strip	Write a summary of a series of events
Comic-Strip Reporter	Write news stories
New Characters	Create new characters for comic strips
Renaming Characters	Create names for comic characters
TV-Show Comic Strip	Analyze TV shows as comic strips
Worthy Topics	Create topics for comic-strip stories
Superperson	Create an imaginary comic-strip character
Farfetched Comic	Develop creative-writing skills
Comic Cut-Up	Create story characters
Comic Mix and Match	Develop creative expression
Balloons	Create comic-strip story lines
Making Up Endings	Create story endings
An Imaginary Dialogue	Create imaginary dialogues
Patent Pending	Create inventions for comic characters
Comic-Strip Party	Develop creative expression
A Class Comic Strip	Create a comic strip about school

PART II: Current Events/Human Behavior

ACTIVITY	OBJECTIVE
Life's Problems	Identify problems and issues of daily life
That's Life	Identify real-life events
Social Problems	Describe social problems
Speak Freely	Identify expression of opinion
We May Disagree	Express an opinion about a controversial issue
News Capsules	Discuss current news stories
Why Read Them?	Analyze the appeal of comic strips
Popularity Poll	Analyze the popularity of various comic strips
Newsprint Shortage	Evaluate current newspaper comic strips
Life Without Comics	Analyze the role of comic strips in our lives
Lifestyles	Describe individual lifestyles
Outer-space Visitor	Analyze comic strips as reflections of life
Facial Expressions	Identify examples of facial expressions
Emotions	Identify various emotions
Stereotypes	Identify instances of stereotyping
Values and Comic Strips	Identify individual values and behavior
I'm Glad You Asked	Analyze personal problems and offer appropriate solutions
Editorial Views	Develop editorial writing skills
Your Opinion Please	State personal views regarding comic-strip issues
Most and Least Like Me	Identify similarities and differences in personal characteristics
You're the Main Character	Illustrate personal characteristics

Suggestions for Implementation

1. Administer The Great Comic Strip Survey (Appendix B) to your students. Their answers will be interesting and will help you plan your lessons.
2. Examine the activities in Appendix A. You may want to include some of them in your program.
3. Before implementing the program, collect as many newspaper comic strips as possible. There are over 300 syndicated comic strips.
4. The activities can be used in a variety of ways. Comic strips, for example, can be used to decorate creative and colorful learning centers.
5. If possible, prepare a comic-strip bulletin board to create interest in your program. Some of the activities ask students to display their work.
6. Examine the sources listed in Appendix C. The two resources by Maurice Horn, for example, are excellent.
7. Consider how you will secure copies of newspaper comic strips for use with your students.
8. All activities are designed to be used with any newspaper comic strips. Since there is a great deal of variation in the comic strips included in different newspapers, none of the activities is tied to a specific newspaper. You may want to add activities or tailor certain activities to your local newspaper.

PART ONE

Language Arts
Creative Writing

Parts of Speech

CAN YOU IDENTIFY PARTS OF SPEECH USED BY COMIC-STRIP CHARACTERS?

Select three comic strips from your newspaper. Identify the words from the comic strips that are nouns, verbs, adjectives, and adverbs. Check your answers with your teacher. Exchange your comic strips with those of some of your classmates to see whether they can get the correct answers.

Use the space below for your answers.

Ridiculous Ralph Ran Rapidly.
(ADJECTIVE) (NOUN) (VERB) (ADVERB)

Nouns	Verbs

Adjectives	Adverbs

Name _____

Adjectives Describe

Adjectives are words used to qualify or limit nouns. Adjectives are words that describe such as silly, funny, dumb, crazy, and happy.

Select any ten comic-strip characters from your newspaper. List the characters along with one or more adjectives that you believe could be used to describe each character. If possible, compare your list with those of some of your classmates.

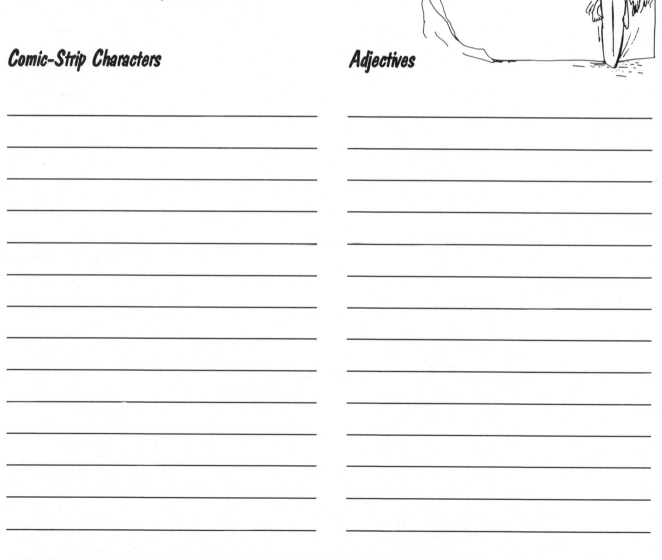

Comic-Strip Characters

_____

_____

_____

_____

_____

_____

_____

_____

_____

_____

_____

Adjectives

_____

_____

_____

_____

_____

_____

_____

_____

_____

_____

_____

Words, Words, Words

CAN YOU IDENTIFY UNFAMILIAR WORDS USED IN THE COMICS?

Read the comic strips in your newspaper every day for one week. Identify at least ten words that are unfamiliar to you. List each word, its definition, and the comic strip in which you found it.

Word	Definition	Comic Strip

Name _____

Poor Grammar

CAN YOU FIND EXAMPLES OF POOR GRAMMAR IN NEWSPAPER COMIC STRIPS?

Read the comic strips in your newspaper every day for at least one week. Identify as many examples of poor or incorrect grammar as you can. List the examples and indicate why they are incorrect.

Examples of Poor Grammar

_____ _____

_____ _____

_____ _____

_____ _____

_____ _____

_____ _____

_____ _____

_____ _____

_____ _____

_____ _____

_____ _____

Substituting Synonyms

CAN YOU SUBSTITUTE SYNONYMS FOR WORDS USED IN VARIOUS COMIC STRIPS?

A synonym is a word that has the same or nearly the same meaning as another word. For example, *joyful, happy,* and *elated* are synonymous words.

Choose five comic strips and substitute a synonym for two words from each one.

Comic Strip	Words	Synonyms

I threw a stone into a lake.
I tossed a rock into a pond.

Main Ideas

CAN YOU IDENTIFY THE MAIN IDEAS OF NEWSPAPER COMIC STRIPS?

Although a newspaper comic strip may include several frames, the comic-strip writer is trying to give only one main idea to the reader.

Select ten comic strips and write the main idea that the writer is trying to communicate to the reader. Write only one sentence for each strip.

Comic Strip	Main Idea

Headlines

CAN YOU SUMMARIZE COMIC-STRIP STORIES BY WRITING NEWSPAPER HEADLINES?

Pretend that each comic strip must have a headline that summarizes the most important information about the comic-strip story. Select at least five comic strips and write a headline for each one. You may want to read a few newspaper headlines to get an idea of how they are written.

Headline	Comic Strip

Name _____

Character Traits

Identify at least five character traits, or personal qualities, shown by comic-strip characters. Identify the trait, the comic character, and the situation.

Excited

Bored

Character Trait	Comic Character	Situation

Clip the characters from the newspaper if you wish.

Name _____

Character Charts

CAN YOU IDENTIFY THE TYPES OF CHARACTERS FOUND IN COMIC STRIPS?

Read all the comic strips in one issue of your newspaper. Make a chart to show the number of men, women, children, animals, and other types of speaking characters included in the comic strips. Use your imagination, but include all of the comic-strip characters.

Use this sheet for your chart.

Types of Characters

_____
_____
_____
_____
_____
_____
_____
_____
_____
_____
_____
_____
_____
_____
_____
_____

Name _____

Character Sketches

CAN YOU WRITE A BRIEF
DESCRIPTION OF A
COMIC-STRIP CHARACTER?

Choose one or more comic-strip characters
from your newspaper, and write at least
two paragraphs describing each character
you've selected. Describe the comic
character as completely as you can. Use the
space below.

This creature has a large
head, legs, eyes, a nose, and mouth.
He or she is obviously very shy.

Comic Strip Character _____

Comic Strip _____

Description _____

_____

_____

_____

_____

Comic Strip Character _____

Comic Strip _____

Description _____

_____

_____

_____

_____

_____

Name _____

Obituary

CAN YOU WRITE A BRIEF DESCRIPTION OF THE LIFE OF A COMIC-STRIP CHARACTER?

Read the obituaries in your newspaper. Pay particular attention to how they are written and what information they include.

Notice that they summarize or describe someone's life. Select at least one comic-strip character and write his or her obituary.

Obituary

Name _____

Novels or Short Stories

CAN YOU SHOW HOW COMIC STRIPS ARE LIKE NOVELS OR SHORT STORIES?

Most comic strips are like novels or short stories in that they include a plot, characters, a setting, action, and a theme.

Select three comic strips that have ongoing stories. Complete the following chart for each comic strip.

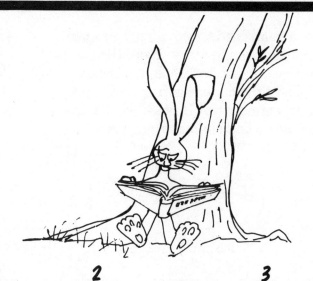

Comic Strips	1	2	3
Plot			
Characters			
Setting			
Action			
Theme			

Name _____

Summary Strip

CAN YOU SUMMARIZE A COMIC-STRIP STORY?

Choose a comic strip from your newspaper that has an ongoing story. Read the comic strip every day for one week. Tell what happened in the comic strip by writing a summary comic strip. If possible, use the actual comic-strip characters in your summary strip and let them discuss the week's events. Cut out or trace the characters to use in your summary strip. Use the space below or the back of this sheet.

MONDAY　　TUESDAY　　WEDNESDAY　　THURSDAY　　FRIDAY　　SATURDAY

　　From *Fun with the Funnies* Copyright © 1983 Scott, Foresman and Company.

Comic-Strip Reporter

CAN YOU WRITE A NEWS STORY ABOUT WHAT HAS HAPPENED IN A COMIC STRIP?

Pretend that you are a news reporter assigned to write a story about what has happened in a comic strip. Read a comic strip and then write a headline and a news story about the events in the comic strip. You may want to read some news stories to get an idea of how to write your story. Remember, a news story should answer the questions who, what, when, where, why, and how.

Use the space at the bottom of this page for your story.

_____

_____

_____

_____

_____

_____

_____

_____

_____

_____

_____

_____

_____

_____

_____

_____

_____

_____

New Characters

CAN YOU CREATE NEW CHARACTERS FOR COMIC STRIPS?

Choose at least three of your favorite comic strips. Keeping the type of story and the present characters in mind, create a new character for each comic strip. Describe the new characters as well as what they would add to the comic strips.

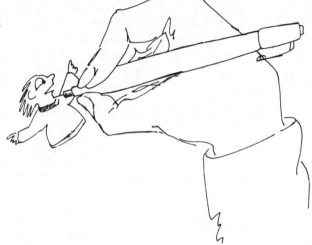

Comic Strip	New Character

From *Fun with the Funnies* Copyright © 1983 Scott, Foresman and Company.

Name _____

Renaming Characters

CAN YOU RENAME COMIC-STRIP CHARACTERS?

Although many comic-strip characters have names or nicknames that reflect what they're like, others do not.

Choose ten comic-strip characters, and after studying what they are like, suggest a new name that is suitable for each character. Share your list of names with one or more classmates to see whether they can guess the characters you've renamed.

Comic-Strip Character

_____
_____
_____
_____
_____
_____
_____
_____
_____
_____

New Name

_____
_____
_____
_____
_____
_____
_____
_____
_____
_____

Character Interviews

CAN YOU DEVELOP SOME INTERVIEW QUESTIONS TO ASK A COMIC-STRIP CHARACTER?

Select at least two comic-strip characters to interview. Pretend that they will answer any questions that you ask.

Develop some questions to ask each character, and write out what you believe would be an appropriate answer for each question. If you wish, ask a classmate your questions and write out his or her answers.

HAVE YOU EVER THOUGHT OF GOING INTO SHOW BUSINESS?

Comic Character	Questions	Answers

From *Fun with the Funnies* Copyright © 1983 Scott, Foresman and Company.

Name _____

TV-Show Comic Strip

CAN YOU IDENTIFY TV SHOWS THAT WOULD MAKE GOOD COMIC STRIPS?

Read the TV schedule in your newspaper. Select at least ten TV shows that you believe would be successful as comic strips. Write a brief description of the shows you chose.

_____

_____

_____

_____

_____

_____

_____

_____

_____

_____

_____

_____

_____

_____

_____

_____

_____

_____

Worthy Topics

CAN YOU IDENTIFY TOPICS THAT WOULD MAKE GOOD SUBJECTS FOR A COMIC STRIP?

There are probably several topics, or subjects, either funny or serious, that you believe would make good comic strips. Identify at least five topics, or subjects, that you would like to see included in a comic strip.

_____

_____

_____

_____

_____

_____

_____

_____

_____

_____

_____

_____

_____

_____

_____

_____

_____

Name _____

Super Person

CAN YOU CREATE A SUPER-PERSON COMIC STRIP?

Using your imagination, create a super-person comic strip. Your super person may have any powers you choose.

In the space below, describe your super person's powers. If possible, draw your character. Describe all the other characters in your comic strip, as well as the setting and story.

_____

_____

_____

_____

_____

_____

_____

Farfetched Comic

CAN YOU CREATE A FARFETCHED COMIC STRIP?

Think about a really farfetched (something unusual from your own imagination) comic strip that you would like to create. Complete the chart on the bottom of this page. You may want to draw an example of the comic strip.

I'M GLAD WE MET I GET TIRED OF FLYING ALONE.

YEAH, BUT ARE YOU SURE YOU'RE A BIRD !?!

Main Character _____

_____

_____

Other Characters _____

_____

_____

Setting _____

_____

_____

What the Comic-Strip Story Is About _____

_____

_____

_____

Name _____

Comic Cut-Up

CAN YOU CREATE A NEW COMIC-STRIP CHARACTER?

The purpose of this activity is to create a new comic-strip character by using parts of other comic-strip characters. For example, what would happen if you combined Superman's head and Snoopy's body, or Hagar's body and Dick Tracy's head?

Clip the characters you want to use from the newspaper. Paste the characters on this sheet and write a brief description of the new character you've created. Name your character.

A New Character

Name _____

Comic Mix and Match

Some interesting and entertaining situations can be developed by mixing comic-strip characters, actions, and settings. For example, what would it be like if Snoopy were Dagwood's dog, Hagar were a patient of Rex Morgan, M.D., or if Donald Duck were Spiderman's best friend?

Develop at least five mix-and-match situations. For each mix and match, describe some interesting things that might happen. If possible, clip the characters from the comic strips and create a new mix-and-match comic strip.

Name _____

Balloons

Select a comic strip from your newspaper and cross out the words in the balloons. Create your own story by writing your own words in the balloons. The story can be serious or funny.

Paste the comic strip on the bottom of this page.

Making Up Endings

CAN YOU DEVELOP ONE OR MORE ENDINGS FOR A COMIC STRIP?

With a little imagination, you can probably write an ending for a comic strip that is as good as the one that was actually used. Select at least three comic strips, cross out the words in the balloons in the last frame, and write in your own ending. Use the bottom and back of this sheet.

Name _____

Imaginary Dialogue

CAN YOU CREATE AN IMAGINARY DIALOGUE (CONVERSATION) BETWEEN COMIC-STRIP CHARACTERS?

Choose ten of your favorite comic-strip characters. Then divide the ten characters into five pairs. Write an imaginary conversation between each pair of characters. For example, if Superman were talking to Mickey Mouse, what might they say to each other?

Character Pairs	Imaginary Conversations

Patent Pending

CAN YOU CREATE AN INVENTION FOR A COMIC-STRIP CHARACTER?

There are many inventions that would be helpful to comic-strip characters. For example, some inventions might help the characters with their problems or weaknesses.

Select five comic-strip characters and carefully study what they are like and what kinds of inventions they could use. Then list the characters and describe the inventions in the space below.

Comic-Strip Characters

DIRT REMOVER

Inventions

_____   _____

_____   _____

_____   _____

_____   _____

_____   _____

_____   _____

_____   _____

_____   _____

_____   _____

_____   _____

_____   _____

_____   _____

_____   _____

_____   _____

Comic-Strip Party

CAN YOU PLAN A PARTY FOR A COMIC-STRIP CHARACTER?

Pretend that you are in charge of preparing a party for your favorite comic-strip character. Decide what kind of party it will be, who will be invited, and what refreshments will be served. In addition, determine the location of the party and make up a list of party games.

Prepare an invitation that includes the above information.

_____

_____

_____

_____

_____

_____

_____

_____

_____

_____

_____

_____

_____

_____

_____

_____

_____

_____

A Class Comic Strip

CAN YOU CREATE A COMIC STRIP ABOUT YOUR SCHOOL AND YOUR CLASSMATES?

Think about a comic strip that uses your school and classmates as the setting and characters. It could be either funny or serious.

In the space below, describe the setting of your class comic strip. In addition, describe the characters and give three or four examples of what kinds of stories you might use for the comic strip.

Setting	Characters	Stories

PART TWO
Current Events
Human Behavior

Name _____

Life's Problems

CAN YOU FIND EXAMPLES OF COMIC-STRIP CHARACTERS WHO ARE FACING SOME OF THE SAME PROBLEMS THAT CONCERN YOU OR YOUR FAMILY?

Read the comic strips in your newspapers for a few days. Find at least five examples of comic-strip characters who are facing various problems of daily life. Some problems might involve money, jobs, crime, or even the weather.

In the space below, identify the problem, the comic strip, and the situation.

Problem	Comic Strip	Situation

Name _____

That's Life

Comic strips often include events that happen in real life. Read the comic strips for two or three days. Identify at least ten events that can happen in real life. In addition, try to identify two or three examples of events that *cannot* happen in real life.

Real-Life Events _____

_____
_____
_____
_____
_____
_____
_____
_____
_____
_____
_____

Unreal Events _____

_____
_____
_____
_____
_____
_____
_____
_____
_____
_____
_____

Name _____

Social Problems

Social problems are sometimes identified in the comic strips. Social problems are problems such as poverty, crime, equal rights, drug abuse, and child abuse.

After reading the comic strips for a few days, identify at least five social problems that you found. List and briefly describe the problems in the space below.

Problems	Descriptions

Name _____

Speak Freely

Our constitution guarantees freedom of speech and freedom of the press. News stories should be truthful and they should avoid including personal opinion. Opinions should be reserved for the editorial pages of the newspaper. Comic strips, however, include many opinions and feelings.

Read the comic strips for one week. Try to find at least five examples of comic-strip characters giving their opinions on an issue. Use a particular comic strip only once.

Comic Character	Opinion

Name _____

We May Disagree

It is common for people to have differing opinions about certain issues. For example, you may disagree with your friends on issues such as how to stop crime or whether there should be a death penalty.

Select an issue that interests you. Then choose your favorite comic strip and cross out the words in the balloons. Pretend that the comic-strip characters are discussing the issue you chose. Draw new balloons and fill them with the words you'd like the characters to say about the issue. Use the bottom and back of this page.

News Capsules

CAN YOU USE COMIC-STRIP CHARACTERS TO SHOW THAT YOU UNDERSTAND AN IMPORTANT NEWS EVENT?

Read the news in your daily paper and select a news story that interests you. Then choose a comic strip that you enjoy. Pretend that the comic-strip characters are discussing the news event. Redraw the comic strip making the characters discuss the news article you've selected. Use the space below.

Current Events/Human Behavior 37

Why Read Them?

CAN YOU DETERMINE WHY COMIC STRIPS ARE SO POPULAR?

Most people read newspaper comic strips. The purpose of this activity is to find out why comic strips are so popular.

Write at least five reasons that people read comic strips. If possible, ask some adults, as well as your classmates, why they read the comics.

Why People Read Comics

1. _____
_____
_____

2. _____
_____
_____

3. _____
_____
_____

4. _____
_____
_____

5. _____
_____
_____
_____

Name _____

Popularity Poll

CAN YOU IDENTIFY THE COMIC-STRIP CHARACTERS THAT ARE THE MOST AND THE LEAST POPULAR?

Clip pictures of ten comic-strip characters from your newspaper and paste them on the bottom of this sheet. Ask at least five of your classmates to rank the characters (1 = most liked, 10 = least liked). Write down the results and write a brief report of your classmates' rankings.

Newspaper Shortage

CAN YOU DECIDE WHICH COMIC STRIPS SHOULD BE INCLUDED IN THE NEWSPAPER?

Pretend that there isn't enough paper available to include all of the comic strips that your newspaper now carries and that your newspaper will have to eliminate half of its comic strips.

Your assignment is to decide which comic strips to keep and which ones to drop. List the names of all the comic strips from one copy of your newspaper and choose which ones you want to see your newspaper keep. Give your reasons in a sentence or two.

Comic Strips	Keep	Don't Keep	Why

Name _____

Life Without Comics

CAN YOU DETERMINE WHAT OUR LIVES WOULD BE LIKE WITHOUT COMIC STRIPS?

Life would go on without the comic strips, but if comic strips were to disappear, many people would feel that something was missing from their lives.

For this activity, pretend that the newspapers have decided to eliminate all comic strips. Your assignment is to write a one-page story titled "Life Without the Comics." Use the bottom and back of this sheet.

Life Without the Comics

_____
_____
_____
_____
_____
_____
_____
_____
_____
_____
_____
_____
_____
_____
_____
_____
_____

Lifestyles

CAN YOU DESCRIBE THE LIFESTYLES OF COMIC-STRIP CHARACTERS?

A person's lifestyle is how he or she lives, including what he or she does during an average day.

Select five comic-strip characters and write a short description of their lifestyles. Describe their jobs, how they live, and the things that are important to them.

Comic Characters	Lifestyle Descriptions

Name _____

Outer-Space Visitor

CAN YOU DETERMINE WHETHER COMIC STRIPS REALLY SHOW WHAT LIFE ON EARTH IS LIKE?

Pretend that you've just landed on earth from another planet and that you are expected to report back about what life on earth is like. But after you land on earth, your spaceship develops problems and you are forced to return home. The only information you find about earth is the comic-strip page of the newspaper.

List ten impressions that you might have about life on earth if the only information you have comes from the comic strips.

1. _____
2. _____
3. _____
4. _____
5. _____
6. _____
7. _____
8. _____
9. _____
10. _____

Facial Expressions

CAN YOU FIND COMIC-STRIP CHARACTERS WHO ARE SHOWING EMOTION IN THEIR FACES?

Study the comic strips and find examples of how facial expressions are used to show emotions. Facial expressions often show emotions such as fear, anger, love, surprise, and boredom. Paste your examples to this sheet.

Emotions

CAN YOU FIND COMIC-STRIP CHARACTERS WHO ARE SHOWING VARIOUS EMOTIONS?

Comic-strip characters show many emotions. Their emotions, or feelings, may include anger, love, sympathy, and fear.

After reading the comic strips for a few days, identify at least ten emotions that have been displayed by comic-strip characters. List the characters and their emotions on this page. You may cut out the characters.

Characters	*Emotions*

Stereotypes

CAN YOU FIND EXAMPLES OF STEREOTYPING IN THE COMIC STRIPS?

Comic strips sometimes stereotype groups or individuals. Stereotyping occurs, for example, when women are shown as nagging housewives or when certain kinds of animals are shown as smart or dumb.

Find at least five examples of stereotyping in the comic strips. Clip the examples and attach them to this sheet. Then describe why your choices are examples of stereotyping.

A-A-A-A-H-H-H-H-H-H

Values and Comic Strips

CAN YOU IDENTIFY THE VALUES OF VARIOUS COMIC-STRIP CHARACTERS?

Comic-strip characters, like all of us, display the positive and negative values of life in our society. Identify one or more characters that display the opposite values listed below:

Comic Characters	Comic Characters
1. Honest	1. Dishonest
2. Hardworking	2. Lazy
3. Brave	3. Cowardly
4. Loud	4. Quiet

I'm Glad You Asked
CAN YOU THINK OF SOME ADVICE TO GIVE COMIC-STRIP CHARACTERS?

Select at least five of your favorite comic-strip characters and think about what you know about each one—about his or her problems and weaknesses.

Write a short sentence or two of advice for each character. You may want to check the advice column in your newspaper for some writing hints.

Character	Advice

Editorial Views

CAN YOU WRITE AN EDITORIAL ABOUT YOUR VIEWS OF THE COMIC STRIPS?

Read the "Editorials" and the "Letters to the Editor" in your newspaper. Write a one-page editorial or letter to the editor in which you give your views about comic strips. Your editorial could describe something that you don't like about comic strips.

_____

_____

_____

_____

_____

_____

_____

_____

_____

_____

_____

_____

_____

_____

_____

_____

Name _____

Your Opinion Please

Give your opinions of the following statements about comic strips:

WHAM!

1. Comic strips include too much violence. _____

_____

_____

_____

2. Comic strips are a bad influence on children. _____

_____

_____

_____

3. Comic strips should include minorities more often. _____

_____

_____

_____

4. Comic strips are a good form of entertainment. _____

_____

_____

_____

Name _____

Most and Least Like Me

WHICH COMIC-STRIP CHARACTERS ARE MOST AND LEAST LIKE YOU?

Think of what you are like as a person. Find five comic-strip characters who are somewhat like you and five characters who are unlike you. List the characters and briefly describe why you made your choices.

Characters Like Me	*Characters Unlike Me*

Name _____

You're the Main Character

CAN YOU DEVELOP A COMIC STRIP ABOUT YOURSELF?

Think about yourself, your friends, your family, your school, and your hobbies and interests. For this activity, develop a comic strip in which you are the main character. In addition, identify and describe other characters, the setting, and the story line, or plot, of your comic strip. Illustrate the comic strip using the space below.

Appendix A

More Activities

1. Form a comic-strip tour company. Determine which comic-strip settings you will visit.
2. Develop a rating system for comic strips similar to the one used for motion pictures.
3. Analyze the literal and figurative language used in comics.
4. Find comic strips that use anachronisms.
5. Find idioms in various comic strips.
6. Identify cause-and-effect relationships in comic strips.
7. After examining the comic strips, list the rules that cartoonists follow in drawing the comics.
8. Identify prefixes and suffixes used in comic strips.
9. Tell why the word *funnies* is not really appropriate to use in describing comic strips.
10. Decide which community organizations various comic-strip characters might belong to.
11. Prepare a news conference of comic-strip characters.
12. Develop a series of New Year's resolutions for various comic-strip characters.
13. Define the word *anthropomorphism* and give examples of how it is used in comic strips.
14. Describe how comic strips have chronicled events in our society.
15. Identify "sound words," or forms of onomatopoeia, in the comics.
16. Select dialogue spoken by comic-strip characters and correct the punctuation by using quotation marks.
17. Write a short composition about why you'd like to be a particular comic-strip character.
18. Locate examples of declarative, exclamatory, and imperative sentences in the comic strips.
19. Pretend that you are a certain comic-strip character and write a short story explaining what it would feel like to be him or her.
20. List specific items or topics that come to mind when you are asked to consider the concept of "comic strips."
21. Identify traits of human nature revealed by the actions of comic-strip characters.
22. Create a full-page newspaper ad for a comic strip you enjoy and that you believe other people should read.
23. Identify the range of jobs or careers of comic-strip characters. Select a particular career or job that would provide interesting material for a new comic strip.
24. Dramatize a real comic strip or write a short play using the characters of a comic strip.
25. Identify how comic-strip characters express their emotions by their use of facial expressions.
26. Predict the next series of events in a continuing-story comic strip.
27. Identify various types of humor (wit, irony, satire, pun) that are present in comic strips.
28. Create a new comic strip by working with a committee of students.
29. Research one or more comic-strip creators.
30. Analyze examples of conflict found in the comic strips.
31. Classify comic strips by their similarities and differences.
32. Analyze the use of animals or objects in comic strips.
33. Write a sports article or feature story in the form of a comic strip.
34. Analyze the degree to which comic strips reflect current American life.
35. Identify comic-strip characters and events that defy the laws of nature.
36. Construct a comic-strip mobile.
37. Summarize the story line of a continuing-story comic strip.
38. Identify statements of fact versus statements of opinion by comic-strip characters.
39. Construct a collage to illustrate some aspect of comic strips.
40. Identify good and bad habits displayed by comic-strip characters.

Appendix B

Name _____

Please answer all questions. Your honest answers will be greatly appreciated. This is not a test; there aren't any right or wrong answers to any of the questions.

School _____

Grade _____

Age _____

Sex _____

1. Do you read the comic strips in your newspaper?

    ____ yes, every day   ____ yes, two or three times a week

    ____ yes, once a week   ____ hardly ever

    ____ no, never

    If you read comic strips at least once a week, please answer the following:

2. List your five favorite comic strips in order of how much you like them.

    1. _____

    2. _____

    3. _____

    4. _____

    5. _____

3. Which comic strip do you like the least?

    _____

4. Do you believe that teachers should use newspaper comic strips in their teaching more than they do now?

    ____ yes

    ____ no

    ____ not sure

Appendix C

Sources and Resources

Ball, Howard. "Who Is Snoopy?" *Language Arts,* October 1976, pp. 798–802.

Berger, Arthur Asa. *The Comic-Stripped American.* New York, N.Y.: Walker, 1973.

Carlson, Julie. "Psst: Teacher's Reading Comics." *Grade Teacher,* December 1969, pp. 28–30.

Dobrowolski, Alex. "The Comic Book Is Alive and Well and Living in the History Class." *The Social Studies,* May/June 1976, pp. 118–120.

Goldgell, Rosanne. "Comics As Textbooks." *Instructor,* March 1977, pp. 129–130.

Hallenbeck, Phyllis. "Remediating With Comic Strips." *Journal of Learning Disabilities,* January 1976, pp. 22–26.

Horn, Maurice. "The Comics: A Cultural History." Pleasantville, New York: Educational Audio-Visual Incorporated, 1976. (Five filmstrips and cassette tapes.)

Horn, Maurice, editor. *The World Encyclopedia of Comics.* New York, N.Y.: Avon Books, 1977.

Kaiserman, Jill. "Comprehension Through Comics." *Learning,* March 1979, p. 64.

Kohl, Herb. "Do Your Own Comics." *Teacher,* January 1977, pp. 12–16.

Kohl, Herb. "Origins: Where Did I Come From? Where Am I Going?" *Teacher,* March 1977, pp. 12–14.

Pierce, Elfrieda. "Word Study: Comic Strip Style." *Learning,* November 1977, p. 48.

Richie, June. "The Funnies Aren't Just Funny." *The Clearing House,* November 1979, pp. 125–128.

Schoof, Robert. "Four-Color Words: Comic Books in the Classroom." *Language Arts,* October 1978, pp. 821–827.

Swain, Emma. "Using Comic Books to Teach Reading and Language Arts." *Journal of Reading,* December 1978, pp. 253–258.

Teff, Thomas. "Motivation: Batman to the Rescue." *Grade Teacher,* March 1968, pp. 12–14.

Thompson, Don, and Lupoff, Dick. *The Comic Book-Book.* New Rochelle, N.Y.: Arlington House, 1973.

Urbani, Trudy. "Fun, Funny, Funnies." *Teacher,* September 1978, pp. 60–68.

Wright, Gary. "The Comic Book—A Forgotten Medium in the Classroom." *The Reading Teacher,* November 1979, pp. 158–161.